SYRACUSE UNIVERSITY 13173777
Our rice village in Cambodia.

W9-DGL-807

DS
534
.42
T66
1963

Our Rice Village in Cambodia

Also by Ruth Tooze

AMERICA
SILVER FROM THE SEA
CAMBODIA

Our Rice Village in Cambodia

BY RUTH TOOZE

Illustrated by EZRA JACK KEATS

NEW YORK · THE VIKING PRESS

Copyright © 1963 by Ruth Tooze and Ezra Jack Keats
All rights reserved
First published in 1963 by The Viking Press, Inc.
625 Madison Avenue, New York 22, N. Y.
Published simultaneously in Canada
by The Macmillan Company of Canada Limited

Library of Congress catalog card number: 63-18364

PRINTED IN THE U.S.A. BY HALLIDAY LITHOGRAPH CORP.

GK19M1634

To Phuon and Neari and the many children
who live in rice villages in Cambodia
and the many American children
who also live in villages—
friends around the world

Our Rice Village in Cambodia

This is our house.
We live in it, my sister Neari and I,
My father and my mother.
We live in our house that stands high on
stilts.

My father built our house.
He made the floor of split bamboo.
He made the roof of palm leaves.
He made the walls of bamboo strips and
palm leaves.

We all helped my father bring the bamboo
    for our house.
He split the bamboo into boards for the
    floor.
He split small strips for the wall, a wall that
    comes up only halfway between the
    floor and the roof, so there is always
    plenty of air.
I helped pile the bamboo ready for work,
    while Neari laid out the palm leaves.

The room beneath our house is another
house.
The cow, the pigs, and the chickens live
in it.
Their floor is earth tramped hard by their
feet.
Our floor makes a roof for them, but they
have no walls.

12

This is the house we live in,
My father and mother, my sister Neari
    and I,
Our cow, the pigs, and the chickens.
All of us live in this house we built.

The sun shines on our house
All day long in the dry season,

A part of each day in the wet season.
The sun shines on us and our house.

The rain washes our house clean.
Many days in the rainy season
The rain comes down from the clouds,
White and gray and purple clouds that
cover our blue sky.

17

The rain and sunshine wash and warm our
house,
Our house standing high on stilts,
Where we live, my father and mother and
Neari and I,
Our cow and the pigs and the chickens.

Our house is in a village
Of many houses just like ours,
With families just like ours,
But many have more children and a few
      have grandfathers and grandmothers.

Near our village are the rice fields,
Where everyone works and plays,
Where the good rice grows for us to eat—
The rice, the good rice.

In May, near the end of the dry season,
The snows melt in the high mountains of
    the north.
Water fills the mountain streams
Which pour into the River Mekong,
    the mighty River Mekong.

We plant the rice seed beds
As we watch for the water coming,
Coming to fill our fields,
The fields for growing rice.

The rains come, the streams are filled.
The mighty Mekong, flowing down through
    the heart of our land,
Overflows its banks and covers our land,
Making fields for growing rice.

My father plows his rice field.
Two strong water buffaloes pull the plow,
    turning the thick mud.
I follow them and let the mud ooze between
    my toes
And laugh at the white bird riding on the
    buffaloes' horns.

The village boys and I bring bunches of
rice shoots to my mother and the
other women,
Who plant the rice shoots in long rows
under the water in the mud.

Day after day they stand knee deep in
    water,
Bending and planting, bending and
    planting, until all the fields are full.

Now it rains almost every day.
The river rises ever higher, pouring more
    and more water over our fields.
The rice shoots grow, and soon the fields
    are green.
Sheets of green rice cover our plains.

28

Neari, too, likes the water.

We wash and swim and play with our
     friends.

We watch the birds in the rice fields:

White ibis, herons, and gulls.

The fish from the river come into our fields.
I catch some fish for our dinner almost
    every day.
I wash in the deep, flowing water in the
    ditch around the field.
I swim and play there too.

In the fall my father and his friends cut
    the ripe rice.
They cut it with curved rice knives.
My father carved the handle of his knife.
He says I am too little to use it.

Then my mother and the women winnow
      the rice,
Tossing the rice in big round woven trays
High in the air, over and over and over,
To shake the kernels free from the husks.

33

Now we have good rice to eat,
And fish and many green vegetables.
We pick bananas from the trees in our
    village,
Papayas and mangoes too.

In the house next door to us lives a big
    brother
Who plays a drum, beating the tight
    drumskin with his hands.
He is my best friend
And the best drummer in our village.

When night comes our village stands in
blackness.
The stars shine in the sky and the moon
grows from a curved sliver to a round
silver ball.
The men of our village build a fire,
A big fire to give us light.

Big brother beats his drum; other boys beat
     their drums loud and soft.
Sareth plays his flute and Tek his
     two-stringed fiddle,
Playing old, old songs we know,
So we may sing and dance.

37

Everyone in the village gathers round the
    fire to sing and dance and listen.
Meng drums and sings so hard the sweat
    covers his brown body
So it shines in the light of the fire,
The light from the stars and the fire in the
    blackness of the night.

The men and women dance our dance,
    the *lampton*,
Their fingers held just so,
Their arms moving in the graceful curves
    of the *lampton*,
Their feet in step with the beat of the
    drums.
My friends and I watch and we dance too.

But the young men and women are the best.
The babies nod their heads and sleep.
The old men and women watch and softly
    clap their hands with the beat of
    the drums.

39

My house, my family, my work, my play,
Our village, our friends, their work,
    their play,
Water and rice and fish, daytime and
    nighttime,
These make our life, our good life in
    Cambodia.